The Queens Don't Settle
Daily Journal

Ace Metaphor

A MESSAGE FROM ACE METAPHOR

"When I was lost, it was these exact exercises that helped me find my way. I hope they provide you with just as much clarity as they provided me."

DAY 1

TODAY'S AFFIRMATION:

1.

_____

_____

ONE GOAL YOU'D LIKE TO ACCOMPLISH TODAY:

1.

_____

DAILY ACTION: Today while you are on your daily journey, find the time to locate a mirror and say "I love you" to your reflection.

ACE QUOTE OF THE DAY -

You know ANY man
would be lucky to have you, right?
So start acting like it...

3

THE SELF LOVE VOWS

Take the next 5 minutes to write five life-long promises to yourself that you vow to never break no matter how good or bad life gets.

1.
_____

2.
_____

3.
_____

4.
_____

5.
_____

Write those self-promises above as inspiration to compose your self-love vows. Consider writing them as if today you were marrying the YOU of your dreams.

_____
_____
_____
_____

RATIONALE: The reason I felt it was important to include this exercise in this journal is because it is important for each of us to promise life-long commitment, love and honor to ourselves prior to making those promises to another person. We should be our first loves. Think about it, we have been there for ourselves since the beginning, shouldn't we reward that loyalty with the promise of life-long love and respect? Additionally, these self-love vows will supercede any other vows made to another person since they will have been recited first. Never forget that. Never settle and bend these vows to yourself to keep vows to others, no matter how hard it gets or how guilty you feel about loving you first.

Below is a self-love contract, which means you agree to keep your self-love vows no matter what. Please sign.

Name:

_____

Date:

_____

Signature:

_____

DAY 2

TODAY'S AFFIRMATION:

1.

_____

_____

ONE GOAL YOU'D LIKE TO ACCOMPLISH TODAY:

1.

_____

DAILY ACTION: Today, start a meaningful conversation with someone new.

ACE QUOTE OF THE DAY -

One day
You will meet a man
And thank God you didn't give up...
Until then,
All you have to do is...
Not give up.

THE SOUL SELFIE

Close your eyes and take an honest snapshot that captures a mental picture of your personality. Use the next five minutes to locate all the blemishes (areas of improvement) on it then jot down the top five below.

1.

2.

3.

4.

5.

Pick one of the blemishes that you wrote down above from your soul selfie and write about it. Consider including how this blemish has affected your life, the lives of others and one or two ways you can "cover it up" with self-love.

RATIONALE: In order to make self improvements, we have to regularly look at our reflections. This helps us to become self-aware. A lack of self awareness is dangerous to our progression as well-rounded whole individuals. Just as it's important to recognize your strengths, it's equally important to be aware of your areas for important. How can you fix a problem area in your personality or character if you never look at it with a critical eye? From here, action plans can be put in place to "make-up" and heal those blemishes that ultimately keep us from enjoying life to the fullest.

DAY 3

TODAY'S AFFIRMATION:

1.

_____

_____

ONE GOAL YOU'D LIKE TO ACCOMPLISH TODAY:

1.

_____

DAILY ACTION: Self appreciation is important. Buy yourself a gift today, doesn't have to be expensive just thoughtful

ACE QUOTE OF THE DAY -

Straighten your crown, sis! A few years from now he is going to try to text you like...
"You're the good one that got away. I don't know what I was thinking."
(Don't reply)
Smirk and think to yourself... You damn right!

THE "ME" DATE

Take five minutes to jot down five components, that if executed correctly, would contribute to the *perfect* local date.

1.
_____

2.
_____

3.
_____

4.
_____

5.
_____

I want you to use some of the perfect date components you mentioned above to write about how you would ideally want your first date to go from start to finish. However, write it from the perceptive of you taking yourself out on a date. Be descriptive.

_____

_____

_____

RATIONALE: "Me" dates are super important! However, most people don't treat it as a special night out. We tend to put much more effort in dates with others than the time we plan out for ourselves. Just as you think about what dress you are going to wear when you go out with him, I want you to think even more about that dress you are going to wear when going out with you! Why wait for someone to think you are special enough to take to that fancy restaurant downtown when YOU know you are SPECIAL and can take yourself to that place you've wanted to go with someone SPECIAL. "Me" dates are how self-love is grown. They remind you that you are loved, valued and appreciated.. Just as you would value a man who spends the time to plan out a nice night weeks in advance for you, self-love will provide the same feeling of adoration. Below I want you to contract to yourself that you will take yourself out on that exact date you described in your entry. Remember YOU are worthy of YOU.

Name:

_____

Date:

_____

Signature:

_____

DAY 4

TODAY'S AFFIRMATION:

1.

_____

_____

ONE GOAL YOU'D LIKE TO ACCOMPLISH TODAY:

1.

_____

DAILY ACTION: Anticipate the challenges your going to face today and say "you're not going to defeat me"

ACE QUOTE OF THE DAY -

God didn't make ANY mistakes when he created you
He gave you that smile
Those goals, that personality
And your heart for a reason...
Never change it just because some "man" doesn't
like it

THE "BLOCK" PARTY

For this exercise put on your favorite musical playlist and pour you a glass of your favorite drink then take the next 10 minutes writing down the name of at least five people you are going to *block* from your social media accounts. Start by auditing family first, then friends, then exs, then random people who post negativity all the time. Do this until you get to five invitations to your *block* party.

Challenge yourself to think of at least one person that's in your "inner" circle that needs to join this list.

1.
_____

2.
_____

3.
_____

4.
_____

5.
_____

Write about the person that was most difficult to add to this block party list and explain why the invitation must be sent.

_____

_____

_____

_____

_____

_____

_____

_____

_____

_____

_____

_____

_____

_____

_____

_____

_____

RATIONALE: Some people don't deserve to have direct access to your life and you know that, but far too often we struggle to make the difficult decision to revoke access to our lives. The inability to move on from certain relationships not only allows the person to keep a key to open the doors of communication and bring negativity back into our lives. It also invites then to have a seat in our minds every time we scroll past their pages on social media. This exercise is asking you to choose you and your peace of mind, even if that means making the tough decision to block someone that you love. Your life will be happier the moment you learn how to locate the block button and use it.

DAY 5

TODAY'S AFFIRMATION:

1.

_____

_____

ONE GOAL YOU'D LIKE TO ACCOMPLISH TODAY:

1.

_____

DAILY ACTION: Park further away from your destination to get some accidental exercise in and use the extra few steps to smile.

ACE QUOTE OF THE DAY -

Sometimes the first step to happiness...
Can be as easy as going to sleep and resisting the urge to text the wrong person.

THE PERFECT MATE

Take the next fifteen minutes to brainstorm ten
qualities the mate of your dreams MUST have and
write them below.

1.

_____

2.

_____

3.

_____

4.

_____

5.

_____

6.

_____

7.

_____

8.

_____

9.

_____

10.

_____

I want you to write about the type of woman this type of man would deserve and the qualities she would display.

_____

_____

_____

_____

_____

_____

_____

_____

_____

_____

_____

_____

_____

_____

_____

_____

RATIONALE: Just as it is important to find the mate of your dreams, it is important for you to become the mate of theirs, before you two meet. This exercise starts the self-conversion needed to explore if you are on the right track to becoming the type of person you desire or if there is some work to be done.

DAY 6

TODAY'S AFFIRMATION:

1.

_____

_____

ONE GOAL YOU'D LIKE TO ACCOMPLISH TODAY:

1.

_____

DAILY ACTION: Throughout the day, consciously count the number of blessings you receive today, no matter how big or small.

ACE QUOTE OF THE DAY -

I'm not trying to be your other half...
I'm trying to be your other WHOLE

I'm not trying to complete you...
I'm trying to double you!

Your wholemate.

THE MENTAL SHOWER

Take the next five minutes to think of 3 times this week that you've had a discouraging thought or feeling about yourself and note those things below.

1.

_____

2.

_____

3.

_____

I want you to take a mental shower by washing away those negative thoughts. First, cross a line through the statements above then write the opposite positive affirmation below. Next pick the thought of discouragement you struggle with the most and give yourself a heart-to-heart pep talk.

_____

_____

_____

_____

_____

_____

_____

RATIONALE: Just as one should take a literal shower daily to wash away the dirt and sweat that's gathered from the activities of the day, one should take the time nightly to meditate and wash away the negative thoughts or feelings we all experience throughout the day. Just as physical dirt can accumulate to a point that a smell can form and keep us away from others, toxic thoughts, if not rinsed daily, can prevent us from getting closer to our goals and dreams and prevent us from finding a genuine connection with someone special. A mindset can be foul smelling also. This is why showering your mind daily is just as important as washing your body. This process will keep your thoughts fresh and your confidence clean and free of sludge, so that you can chase the opportunities of success before you.

DAY 7

TODAY'S AFFIRMATION:

1.

ONE GOAL YOU'D LIKE TO ACCOMPLISH TODAY:

1.

DAILY ACTION: Think of a person that you are thankful to have in your life and text them "thank you"

ACE QUOTE OF THE DAY -

It's so important to be FRIENDS first...
Because in a relationship, lust will eventually die, romantic love will sway and sexual attraction will come and go...

But it is your ability to love that person as a FRIEND that will keep you both together through the tough times.

LETTER TO A PRINCESS

For the next five minutes, I want you to think of a specific day in your life between five and ten years ago and write the approximate date down below.

Date:

_____

I want you to pretend that you could send a letter back in time to that very date and that your former self would be able to read it. What would that letter say? Write it below.

_____

_____

_____

_____

_____

_____

_____

_____

_____

_____

_____

_____

RATIONALE: The are so many lessons that can be learned from looking back on the good and bad times of the past. In your letter, did you choose to impart some words of wisdom to your younger self or maybe you chose to provide comfort. Regardless of what you choose to write, the real testimony is in the fact that you are still here able to share the lessons you've learned along the way.

DAY 8

TODAY'S AFFIRMATION:

1.

_____

_____

ONE GOAL YOU'D LIKE TO ACCOMPLISH TODAY:

1.

_____

DAILY ACTION: Try something new today.

ACE QUOTE OF THE DAY -

You are someone's future WIFE
Not future longtime girlfriend, side piece or baby momma!
Never accept anything less

THE STANDARDS CONTRACT

For the next five minutes, I want you to rank the top
five must-have qualities you are looking for from a
mate. Only include the qualifications you absolutely
can't live without.

1.

_____

2.

_____

3.

_____

4.

_____

5.

_____

Write about a time when you settled for a person
who did not possess each of those qualities and how
that affected the relationship.

_____

_____

_____

_____

_____

RATIONALE: There is a huge difference between needs and wants. Wants are qualifications we prefer, while needs are minimum requirements a person must have to even get considered! They are the non-negotiables, but too often people are interviewing prospective mates without first knowing the qualities that fit their souls. Just as a company would determine an area of need, create a position description that includes needed skills before deciding to look for applicants, the same is true for how you should handle your dating life. The worst thing, as you wrote about before, is giving the job of mate to a person that doesn't have the skills needed to keep it. This is how your time is wasted! When you settle, you suffer in the long-run. Below is a standard contract. I want you to make a signed promise to yourself that you will not bend when it comes to those five things ever again in life.

Name:

_____

Date:

_____

Signature:

_____

DAY 9

TODAY'S AFFIRMATION:

1.

_____

_____

ONE GOAL YOU'D LIKE TO ACCOMPLISH TODAY:

1.

_____

DAILY ACTION: For a moment, I want you to hold your arm straight out and make a fist. Afterwards, think of every negative thought you've had and allow your energy to move those thoughts toward that fist. Once they are all collected there, open your fist and *allow* yourself to let go of all that negativity.

ACE QUOTE OF THE DAY -

Beware,
Just because a man enters your life...
Does not mean he is the one you prayed for

WHO HURT ME?

For the next five minutes, I want you to ask yourself
"Who hurt me?" and write down the first five
people that immediately come to mind.

1.

_____

2.

_____

3.

_____

4.

_____

5.

_____

I want you to pick the people for that letter that
deserves forgiveness the least and write them a
letter of forgiveness anyway.

_____

_____

_____

_____

_____

_____

RATIONALE: In order to move forward in our lives, we have to forgive the people who hurt us, even those who have done nothing to earn our forgiveness. Holding on to hurt does nothing but weigh us down. Some think that forgiving people who don't deserve is doing something for that person, when in fact you are doing something for your heart, mind and soul. Forgiveness is letting go. In the letter you wrote, I hope that it helps you find peace and that in this very moment you feel lighter than before.

Side note: ***Don't confuse forgiving someone with giving someone a second chance, nah!***

DAY 10

TODAY'S AFFIRMATION:

1.

_____

_____

ONE GOAL YOU'D LIKE TO ACCOMPLISH TODAY:

1.

_____

DAILY ACTION: Find an old photo today and reflect on those memories for a moment and appreciate the journey.

ACE QUOTE OF THE DAY -

Sometimes the way to stop loving someone that you shouldn't...
Is to start loving someone you should...
Which is YOU
Love You.

I LOVE ME!

For the next five minutes, I want you to think about all the things you love about yourself and write down the first ten things that come to mind.

1.

_____

2.

_____

3.

_____

4.

_____

5.

_____

6.

_____

7.

_____

8.

_____

9.

_____

10.

_____

Write yourself a love letter.

RATIONALE: To just know that you love yourself is not enough! Just as you expect someone who loves you to say and show it, self-love requires the same. Writing yourself a love letter is a great way to keep your self-love muscle strong! It is with conscience effort that the love for ourselves is grown. Never stop proving to you how much you love yourself.

DAY 11

TODAY'S AFFIRMATION:

1.

_____

_____

ONE GOAL YOU'D LIKE TO ACCOMPLISH TODAY:

1.

_____

DAILY ACTION: Distance yourself from all media for 30 minutes and go out and explore nature.

ACE QUOTE OF THE DAY -

40 years from now…
You won't be thinking about the guy
That did you wrong and left, no…
You will be too busy loving the man
That did you right and STAYED…

DON'T WASTE MY TIME!

For the next five minutes, I want to write down the last ten people you have messaged (text or DM) and write them down below.

1.

2.

3.

4.

5.

6.

7.

8.

9.

10.

I want you to go back to that list and write spend "more time" with or spend "less time" with next to each name then pick one person you felt you should spend more time with and one person you felt you should spend less time with and write why.

_____

_____

_____

_____

_____

_____

_____

_____

_____

_____

_____

_____

_____

_____

_____

_____

RATIONALE: The people we choose to surround ourselves with will have a major effect, for better or worse, on the trajectory of our lives. Therefore It is important for us to periodically audit the people we communicate with regularly and decide if the time we use to be their "friend" is getting us closer to our goals or further away from them. Think about it, there are probably "friends" in your contact list that only hit you up when they need something, those are the people you should consider spending less time with and to the contrary, there are people who always have your best interests in mind and always keep it real. Those are the people you should consider spending more time with.

DAY 12

TODAY'S AFFIRMATION:

1.

_____

_____

**ONE GOAL YOU'D LIKE TO ACCOMPLISH
TODAY:**

1.

_____

DAILY ACTION: Do your housework to your favorite playlist and have a dance party.

ACE QUOTE OF THE DAY -

Don't watch an action,
Watch HABITS and PATTERNS...

THE INTERVIEW

For the next five minutes, write down five questions you would ask a potential mate to discern if they are the one for you.

1.

_____

2.

_____

3.

_____

4.

_____

5.

_____

I want you to answer those exact questions yourself in detail as if someone was asking them of you.

_____

_____

_____

_____

_____

_____

RATIONALE: When searching for a potential mate it is important for us to know those open ended questions that allow a person to answer from the heart. These answers, if answered honestly, will help us discern if that person is right for us. Yes, having fun and dates are important, but remember that dates are extended interviews. The point of being there is to find out if that person knows how to "do the job" and asking the right questions can help you discern that.

DAY 13

TODAY'S AFFIRMATION:

1.

_____

_____

ONE GOAL YOU'D LIKE TO ACCOMPLISH TODAY:

1.

_____

DAILY ACTION: Get to work fifteen minutes earlier and use that extra time to mentally prepare for the work day.

ACE QUOTE OF THE DAY -

You will always be too much of a woman...
For a guy that's not much of a man...

FORGIVENESS UNIVERSITY

Take the next ten minutes and think of the five biggest mistakes you have made in your life then write them down below

1.

_____

2.

_____

3.

_____

4.

_____

5.

_____

I want you to write about one lesson each of those mistakes taught you. For extra credit, if there is still one of those mistakes you haven't forgiven yourself for, say out loud "I forgive me."

_____

_____

_____

_____

_____

RATIONALE: There is a lesson wrapped in every trial and tribulation we experience and its important for us to learn what our mistakes are trying to teach us. Do not go through all that pain and hurt for nothing. Learn from it! Make it a point to revisit your shortcomings often and extract as many areas of improvement you can. This is how you not only become a better person but also, ensure that you don't keep repeating the same mistakes over and over again.

DAY 14

TODAY'S AFFIRMATION:

1.

_____

_____

ONE GOAL YOU'D LIKE TO ACCOMPLISH TODAY:

1.

_____

DAILY ACTION: Take the next two minutes to clear your mind by focusing on inhaling and exhaling

ACE QUOTE OF THE DAY -

Before you let a man
sweep you off your feet...
Be sure he's prepared to catch you when you fall...
You might be TOO much woman for him!

THE SELF-APPRAISAL

From 1-10, 1 being the worst level of YOU you can be and 10 being the best level of YOU you can be, I want to rate how well you are currently performing as a person

1.

_____

I want you to take that number and write down an action plan full of controllable factors to get that self-appraisal number one point higher by next week.

_____

_____

_____

_____

_____

_____

_____

_____

_____

RATIONALE: Self-awareness is so important! Doing regular self-appraisals and assigning it a numeric value is a great way to identify problem areas and mark progress on the journey to improve them.

DAY 15

TODAY'S AFFIRMATION:

1.

_____

_____

ONE GOAL YOU'D LIKE TO ACCOMPLISH TODAY:

1.

_____

DAILY ACTION: Hug yourself in a crowded room today just because.

ACE QUOTE OF THE DAY -

In order to begin healing…
You MUST remove the person that keeps hurting you!
You can NOT skip this part of the process

I'M NOT CHANGING!

For the next five minutes, think of five things about yourself that you love so much, you're not changing for anybody.

1.

2.

3.

4.

5.

Choose the quality you love most about yourself from above and write why maintaining it means so much to you.

RATIONALE: The right person for you will love who you are and won't try to change you and included in those "right people" is you. You are the right person for you so be sure to love yourself enough to embrace the things that make YOU you.

DAY 16

TODAY'S AFFIRMATION:

1.

_____

_____

ONE GOAL YOU'D LIKE TO ACCOMPLISH TODAY:

1.

_____

DAILY ACTION: Tonight plan to be in bed for thirty minutes earlier than normal. Use the extra time in bed to just lay.

ACE QUOTE OF THE DAY -

Want me?
Earn me!

NO FREE SAMPLES

For the next five minutes, I want to think about the things that you will only do for your future husband and write at least five of those things below.

1.
_____

2.
_____

3.
_____

4.
_____

5.
_____

I want you to reflect on a time when you were tempted (or did) give those wifely benefits to a boyfriend and why you feel that you did.

_____
_____
_____
_____
_____

RATIONALE: We have to have boundaries when it comes to dating. This includes not only our standards and expectations but also limits the pieces of ourselves we give people prior to having a life-long commitment. This means that even though you may have a giving heart, you ain't *giving IT away* to someone until they say "I do." This is where self-discipline comes into place. We have to make up our minds prior to getting into relationships as to which parts of our spirit are off limits during the dating phase and hold steadfast no matter how great that person appears to be. No free samples.

DAY 17

TODAY'S AFFIRMATION:

1.

_____

_____

ONE GOAL YOU'D LIKE TO ACCOMPLISH TODAY:

1.

_____

DAILY ACTION: Reconnect with a valued friend from the past. Send them a text and ask how they are doing.

ACE QUOTE OF THE DAY -

Stop lowering your standards…
For people too lazy
To UP their qualifications!

THE PURPOSE PYRAMID

For the next ten minutes, I want you to think of three overall life goals that you and your potential partner must have in common in order to grow closer.

1.

_____

2.

_____

3.

_____

I want you to visualize a day in the future when you and your future husband are now elderly and have finally accomplished those common life goals together. Write about what that moment will look like.

_____

_____

_____

_____

_____

RATIONALE: I believe that in order for two people to draw closer to each other over a lifetime and still maintain their individual happiness, they have to have life goals in common because those shared goals give them purpose and direction. Imagine a pyramid, as long as both parties are always walking toward a purpose at the peak, they will draw closer to one another. When couples neglect having anything in common, they often may draw closer to each other but never find true fulfillment with each other. This can cause unhappiness or a desire to keep chasing an unfulfilled purpose and the relationship suffers. Two people heading in different directions a rift in the relationship and people grow apart. Know your purpose and find someone whose purpose is close to yours, so that the two of you get closer simply by chasing it.

DAY 18

TODAY'S AFFIRMATION:

1.

_____

_____

**ONE GOAL YOU'D LIKE TO ACCOMPLISH
TODAY:**

1.

_____

DAILY ACTION: Put on your "good clothes"
today for no reason.

ACE QUOTE OF THE DAY -

Life is to short
To be left on "seen"
Get you an always-texter-backer
Life is better that way, trust me

I'M THANKFUL FOR...

For the next ten minutes, I want you to think of the five most influential people in your life and write them down below.

1.
_____

2.
_____

3.
_____

4.
_____

5.
_____

I want you to write a letter of gratitude to that person.

_____

_____

_____

_____

_____

RATIONALE: It so easy to overlook the people that matter to us the most. Often we start to take them for granted, not maliciously but because of absent mindedness. Try reflecting on those you are most thankful for weekly.

DAY 19

TODAY'S AFFIRMATION:

1.

_____

_____

ONE GOAL YOU'D LIKE TO ACCOMPLISH TODAY:

1.

_____

DAILY ACTION: If someone asks you "How are you today?" be honest no matter how difficult

ACE QUOTE OF THE DAY -

I'd rather be called petty than foolish...
I will block socials,
Unsave numbers
And delete text threads in a heartbeat...
I love myself too much to be mistreated

THE GIVE-A-F BUDGET

For the next five minutes, I want you to write the last five things that you shouldn't have gave a F about but you did anyway.

1.

_____

2.

_____

3.

_____

4.

_____

5.

_____

I want to choose one of the situations above and write about why you chose to care so much about something that shouldn't have bothered you or mattered to you in the first place.

_____

_____

_____

_____

_____

RATIONALE: We have to start budgeting our Fs. We cannot give everyone the energy and time of day just because they intrude on our lives with their negativity. When we start to budget our Fs, we stop giving Fs to people who don't deserve them and save our cares for people who truly need and value them.

DAY 20

TODAY'S AFFIRMATION:

1.

_____

_____

ONE GOAL YOU'D LIKE TO ACCOMPLISH TODAY:

1.

_____

DAILY ACTION: Drink an extra glass of water today.

ACE QUOTE OF THE DAY -

You can love HARD and still love wrong…
Loving APPROPRIATELY
Is the only way to love right!

EAR TO EAR

For the next five minutes, think about the last five times you smiled from ear to ear and write those times below

1.

2.

3.

4.

5.

Choose one of those times above and write every detail about it as if you were describing a picture in vivid detail.

RATIONALE: Whenever life makes you sad, I want you to come back to this journal and read this entry.

DAY 21

TODAY'S AFFIRMATION:

1.

_____

_____

ONE GOAL YOU'D LIKE TO ACCOMPLISH TODAY:

1.

_____

DAILY ACTION: Do something that makes you smile today.

ACE QUOTE OF THE DAY -

Your heart is a prize
Not a participation trophy

CLOSE THE CHAPTER

For the next twenty minutes, I want you to think of ten people, thoughts, feelings and ideas that you are NOT going to take into tomorrow and beyond.

1.

_____

2.

_____

3.

_____

4.

_____

5.

_____

6.

_____

7.

_____

8.

_____

9.

_____

10.

_____

I don't want you to write anything, I simply want you to fold this page, close that chapter of your life and do the activity on the next page.

In place of doing a journal activity today, I want you to choose your favorite journal activities from the past three weeks and make your own journal schedule for the next seven days. Feel free to improvise and free write as needed. Love you all. Thanks for allowing me to be a part of your last 21-days.